18. 12. 83

Ellen and Jack

We send you a littel
memory of a pleasent
visit and a wonderful
time together

from all the family
    in Kinnert

WILD FLOWERS
OF THE HOLYLAND

WILD FLOWERS

Uzi Paz

OF THE HOLYLAND

CHARTWELL BOOKS INC.

Translation: Ilana Shiloh

ISBN 0–89009–227–3

Published by Chartwell Books Inc.
A Division of Book Sales Inc.
110 Enterprise Avenue
Secaucus, New Jersey 07094

Introduction

There exists an inverse ratio between the long history of Israel and the size of the country. Israel is indeed a small country, hard to spot on the map. But in spite of its smallness, it is rich in the variety of its landscapes and natural resources.

We find here, side by side, high mountains and deep valleys (the Hermon is about 3000 m. high and the Dead Sea — 392 m. below sea-level); tangled woods and arid desert areas; steep cliffs and sandy plains; narrow, tortuous canyons and wide riverbeds, filling occasionally with flood waters; treacherous sand-dunes and treacherous marshes.

All these varieties of landscape are matched by a variety of flora and fauna. In Israel there are found about 3,000 genera of plants (apart from the bryophytes, algae and fungi); 150 of them are endemic, i.e. — particular to the terrain of Israel.

What accounts for that richness is the geographic location of the country. It is a nexus between Asia and Africa; it lies between the Mediterranean and the desert. Therefore it includes the representatives of the different continents and climatic zones.

The north of the country enjoys 500–1000 mm. of rainfall in winter (from November to April); its flora is therefore similar to that of other Mediterranean countries, like Greece, Turkey, the south of France and Spain on the European side and the slopes of the Atlas mountains on the African side.

This Mediterranean zone is surrounded, from the south and east, by a narrow belt of steppe, extending from the plateaus of central Asia. Here the vegetation resembles that of the plateaus in Turkey, Iraq and Iran.

Still more to the south we find the arid desert areas, originating in the Arabic Peninsula. Here, rainfall is minimal and, in some years, nil.

The main flowering season in Israel is spring, because of the optimal conditions of temperature and soil at that time of year; yet the variety of climate and soil enables a continuous blooming during all 12 months. In the light soils of the coastal plain the flowering begins a short time after the first rains; it tardies in the hills and the heavy soils of the valleys; it lasts till midsummer along the seashore, the streamcourses and in the marshes.

Another factor contributing to the continuity of floral growth is the existence of geophytic plants, which compose 10% of the vegetation. The bulbs and tubers are underground storages of nutrition and enable the blossoming of geophytes in times when other plants have long wilted. Thus the succession of flowering is never stopped, and this album testifies to its colorfulness, variety and richness.

In spite of man's artificial interference, the flora and fauna of Israel have remained basically the same since the days of the Bible. We can still find here "the cedars of Lebanon", "the tamarisk in the desert" and "the hyssop that springs out of the wall"; but the Bible is obviously not a textbook of natural history and all its descriptions of nature are not introduced for the sake of scientific accuracy but are destined to serve as a background for the social, moral and religious messages.

There is no correlation between the occurrence of a plant in Israel and the number of times it is mentioned in the Bible. Some plants are referred to many times, others — not at all. Of all the Israeli flowers only two are specifically mentioned — "the rose of Sharon" and "the lily of the valley" (Song of Solomon, 2:1). Besides, there is no certainty that a given name always refers to the same specimen. We may infer this from the habit of Arab shepherds to give entirely different plants the same name and inversely — give the same plant different names in different regions.

We may also assume that certain names are merely a literary metaphor; "thorn and thistle" refer to noxious weeds in general; "briers and thorns" refer to wasteland; "reed and bulrush" refer to any marshy vegetation.

The 2000 years of Diaspora have made the people forget most facts about the climatic conditions, flora and fauna of their homeland. Most commentators of the Bible lived in Europe and tried to project the knowledge of their native parts on the Biblical text; but such attempts are obviously bound to be misinterpretations.

All in all, the Bible mentions about 100 various plants, and most of them only once. Therefore, apart from "the seven kinds" with which the land was blessed and "the four kinds" of plants used on the Feast of Tabernacles', all other identifications of the flora mentioned in the Bible are not verifiable.

HARBINGERS
OF THE RAIN

Oppressive heat is still everywhere, baking the hills, fields and waysides. But the summer is drawing to a close: the evenings are imperceptibly cooler and the nights often quite dewy, sunsets more vivid and beautiful. Suddenly in mid-August — as though to herald the coming of fall — the tall white spikes of the sea squill grow up out of the parched earth and from among the dried clumps of weedy thistles. Such flowering seems exotically out of place in this season; indeed, most of the flowers of Israel bloom in the early spring, while some others appear even earlier after the first drizzles of winter.

However, there are ten species of plants in Israel which have dispensed with the prerequisite of rain for flowering. These harbingers of winter bloom in all parts of the country — from the Galilean hills in the north, through the coastal plain and valleys, to the arid steppes of the Negev — before there is the slightest sign of rain. The sea squill is the best known and, by far, the most dramatic of these plants.

This curious phenomenon of estival blooming depends upon a combination of specific conditions fulfilled by the group of plants called geophytes. These are plants which store up nutrients in fleshy subterranean bulbs or tubers during the season of green leafy growth in winter and spring. Although the only visible sign of geophytes during the dry summer are wilted dry leaves, floral and leaf buds are developing and differentiating underground at the expense of the stored nutrients. By summer's end, a tiny plant with miniature flowers and leaves is ready to burst out into the light.

It is the combination of lower temperature and humidity which triggers the blooming, each species having its own particular requirements. Most geophytes do require some rain to bloom; the grape hyacinth needs only a few drops of rain to show its flowers and leaves, while the narcissus take a little longer. The various irises are more sluggish, and begin to bloom only in late spring. Not so the harbingers of winter. The cooler evenings and dewy nights suffice to force out the blooms (but not the leaves which appear in winter). These late summer flowers are visited by the insects, pollinated, ripen seeds and disperse them in time for the rains to sprout the seedlings.

Sea squill (1) — herald of the coming rains.

2   *Like a splash of egg yolk, sternbergia (2) opens*
       just above the ground even before the green
       leaves appear.

Although named Jerusalem meadow saffron (3), this early bloomer is commonly found in the basalt earth of the Golan and eastern Galilee.

The spathe leaf of the biarum (5) conceals tiny flower parts within and invites insect visitors.

Autumn squill (4) flowers hardly reveal the fact that the underground bulb contains a poison.

4

5

6

On sandstone cliff of the Carmel coast are
found the delicate and modest late-flowering
narcissus (6).

More modest and scentless, the small-flowered
pancratium (7) is not as famous as its sister the
sea lily.

8   *When there is a faded dryness around, the fruit
of the smilax becomes happy and glows with
redness (8).*

FLOWERS OF AUTUMN

Of all the diverse changes and permutations of the Israeli landscape, the onset of the rainy season brings the swiftest and most intense. Suddenly, in place of the dry grayish aspects of late summer, a green mantle covers the refreshed fields and hill terraces, trees and shrubs shake off their brittle dry look and are vitalized, the air itself seems to be clarified and charged with vigor.

The rains usually first come in October or November, soaking the ground and reaching the seeds which have lain dormant in the earth during the long summer. The grasses sprout most quickly, providing the greenish lawn. Not far behind, the other kinds of annuals — the pulses, heron's bills, composites, and so on — sprout their two tiny seed leaves which remain hidden for the time being under the dried skeletons of last year's plants. Modest also are the leaflets of the perennial plants, showing the first signs of renewed growth. More conspicuous are the sea squills' and asphodels' green fresh leaves. This now is the "spring of vegetation", but it is modest compared with what is yet to come.

Although flowers are not wanting, they are not always obvious and must be sought out. Among the first to bloom in the short time before the cold temperatures of midwinter inhibit growth are the geophytes, which draw on their reserves stored in underground bulbs. Only four or five rainy days suffice for the grape hyacinth to flower. Not long afterwards appear the pinkish flowers of Steven's meadow saffron, and then comes the winter crocus. Flowers of narcissus and cyclamen can already be found in December; the latter will continue to charm in woodland rock crevices until late spring. The composite pinkish flowers of daisy and the yellowish orange ones of Thrincia *can be found in December growing up from leaf rosettes among the brambly tangle of the burnet — the "queen of the scrubland." These composites have thick root stocks which, like bulbs and tubers, provide them with nutrients to "steal the march" on other flowering plants.*

By January, the winter cold has deepened so much that most native trees shed their leaves and the early bloomers disappear one after another. In early mornings, a frost is detected on the gree shoots; midwinter dormancy descends upon the plant world which awaits reawakening with spring days.

*With white petals and golden crown, the
pheasant's-eye polyanthus narcissus (9) is truly
"queen of the fen."*

Pinkish Steven's meadow saffron (10) appear in hill and dale after the first rains, to be joined a little later by the white goblets of winter crocus (11).

Spikenard and saffron; *calamus and cinnamon, with all trees of frankincense; myrrh and aloes, with all the chief spices.*

SONG OF SOLOMON 4, 14

So profuse, so beautiful and fragrant, and so prolonged in their flowering season, cyclamens (12) are most beloved. ▶

Growing under spiny clumps of burnet, the lovely little daisy (14) is fresh and charming in early winter.

Not as gorgeous as other irises, the Palestine iris (13) blooms before them all.

Jack-in-the-pulpit (15) is modest, but found in profusion near fences and between rocks.

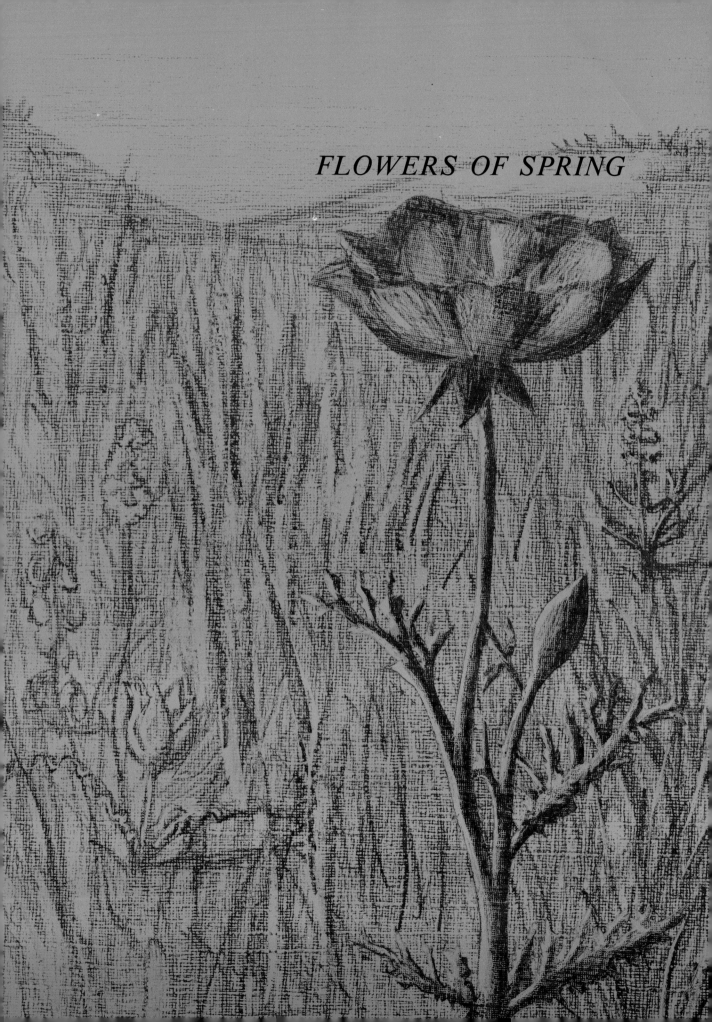

FLOWERS OF SPRING

From mid-February until the end of April (or more exactly when the first "sharav" comes), the country is covered with a mantle of flowers and leafy growth. This is when "the winter is past, the rain is over and gone, the flowers appear on the earth, the time of the singing of the birds is come."

This is not to say that flowers are lacking in other seasons, but even the most casual observer is impressed now with the abundance of floral display. Hundreds of kinds of herbs, shrubs, climbers and trees — some common and plentiful, some rare and even unusual — contribute their part to the spring symphony of color and fragrance.

When does the spring really begin? Though this may vary from year to year — from late January to March — the progression of its appearance in different regions is predictable. Spring comes earliest to the Negev where it is fleeting, while in the Galilee hill country it is tardiest and tends to linger longer. The succession of flowering has its own inner order.

Tradition marks the beginning of spring in Israel with the flowering of the almond, which is so closely connected with the "breaking of the winter cold." After this, new kinds of plants daily burst into bloom — producing a succession of yellow, red, white and purple colors. The earliest guard includes the anemones, groundsel and marigold, whose place is taken by the different kinds of wild orchids, crucifers and pulses. Later the grasses grow up and contribute their part to the green color. As the season advances, the colors fade and become sparser — a sign of the coming summer. It is then that the late bloomers — the irises, lily, michauxia, bellflower and snapdragon — appear along with the woody plants which add their part to the flowering.

Spring begins with the sudden blaze of almond flowers (16).

...and brought forth buds, and bloomed blossoms, and yielded almonds.

NUMBERS 17, 8

17

The first reds of spring are provided by the anemone (18), which is joined in certain regions by blue, white and pink varieties (17).

20

Nowhere else in the world except the sandy coastal plain of Israel are the dark-purple iris (19) and the Tel-Aviv garlic (20) found.

21   *Up in the hills under groves of olive trees, the lesser crowfoot (21) flourishes.*

22

The few round-leaved cyclamens (22) on Mt. Meron are revered by a select circle of nature lovers.

g's spear (23) adds its golden
*ge to fields, while blue lupine
colors the slopes of hills.*

Purple is uncommon among wildflowers; among the few adding this color to the landscape are purple grape hyacinth (25) and hyacinth squill (26).

The Sharon tulip (27) rivals its relatives, the cultivated tulips of Holland, in beauty.

27

Common chrysanthemum (28) is the most profuse and robust of the many yellow wildflowers of spring. Also taking part in the yellow shading are spring groundsel (29), Palestine marigold (30) and prolific scabious (31), each in its season.

32   *Here is the lovely dark red Jerusalem sage (32)*
      whose leaves are prized in cooking by country
      folk.

From among the thirty different kinds of wild orchids in Israel, Anatolian orchid (33) is the one most likely to be encountered by the enthusiast.

34   *Red corn poppies (35), known so well in Europe and North America,*
run wild as well in Asian fields, where viper's bugloss (34) forms a
bluish purple counterpoint.

Another wave of red, but not so widely distributed, is provided by the Aleppo horned poppy (36).

Oriental crowfoot (37), growing in scrublands, looks like a piece of shiny laquerwork.

38

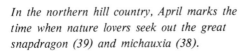

In the northern hill country, April marks the time when nature lovers seek out the great snapdragon (39) and michauxia (38).

If you want to see a Madonna lily (41) in its
natural habitat, seek it out in hidden places in
the western Galilee and on Carmel.

Bristly hollyhocks (42) — higher than a man at the time of the grain harvest.

SPRING IN THE NEGEV

Botanists list about 600 species of flowering plants in the Negev. However, one may travel a dozen times from Beer Sheba to Eilat and only see vast spaces containing here and there an isolated acacia tree or saltbush. The harsh conditions of the arid steppe and desert of the Negev dictate a special rate of flowering which depends intimately upon the slightest increase in precipitation.

If spring is considered as a time of blossoming and fruiting, then it is indeed a rare occurrence in the Negev. There are years, and not few, that plants hardly germinate; in other years the rare sprouts not gobbled up by the ravenous flocks grow no more than a few inches in height, produce a few leaflets and a flower or two.

But there are other years when winter clouds manage to reach the southern latitude and the rain — even only a few inches — falls like a magic wand to awaken hundreds of kinds of plants into growth. It is then that spring comes in a sudden rush: the seeds of annuals germinate; geophytes, tided over difficult times in underground bulbs, leaf out; perennial woody plants, which seemed more dead than alive in this difficult land, sprout leaves and flowers.

During these rare springs, the vast loess steppes of the northern Negev are covered with yellow fields of lion's leaf flowers and carpets of Achillea with purplish patches of wooly salvia; above these rise the red horned poppy, as well as cotton thistle and netted henbane. The barren slopes have now a purplish cover of crucifers (Matthiola and Reboudia) accompanied by thistle and rose dock. On the elevations, the sun rose and wooly stock's bill together with asphodeline form a flowering garden worthy of more temperate climes; it is here we can find the red desert tulip. The sand dunes contain many kinds of Astragulus, Neurada and Dipcadi, but their crowning glory is undoubtedly the Negev iris. The stoney beds of the wadis are filled now with the purple-pink flowers of Zilla; here too we can find the composite Aaronsohnia Factorovskyi (whose main distinction is its "composite" name of two pioneer Israeli botanists) along with the odorous Pulicaria and several species of showy-flowered Fagonia.

Into the short period of four or five weeks is crowded the whole life cycle of these and many other Negev plants. All this beginning in early February; all is over by the end of March — germinating and vegetative growth, flowering and fruiting. The only remains of this fleeting and hasty spring are the seeds which must wait a year or two, or more, for the next rain.

Even as the white broom (43) sheltered the prophet Elijah when he fled to the wilderness (I Kings 19:4), so too today it is an outstanding feature of the desert landscape.

But he (Elijah the Prophet) went a day's journey into the wilderness, and came and sat down under a broom-bush.

I KINGS 19, 4

44

*Purple corn flag (44) grows wild in the
wilderness of Arad, while Mary's iris (45) is
confined to the sand dunes of the western Negev.*

Bursting out of the parched earth, the desert broomrape (46) sucks its sustenance from the roots of other plants.

Found in all parts of the country, lion's leaf (47) nevertheless monopolizes the loess soils of the north of the Negev.

48

49

Hirsute stork's bill (48) flowers open in the morning and are gone by noon, leaving a long "bill" of seeds.

On the rocky slopes of the wilderness, the sun rose (49) flowers only by day.

Not the flowers, but the fruits of rose dock (50) have these conspicuous pinkish segments.

*Confined to oases and
other hot watered places,
the Sodom apple (51)
originated in the tropics.*

WOODLAND FLOWERS

The tourist passing by the woods of the different sections of the Galilee, the forests of the Judean Hills or the groves of Adulam in the south will probably only notice the solid green mass of the trees. However, the hiker who has plunged into the woody tangle, breathed its scents and tasted its fruits, been dampened by its dews and quenched his thirst in the waters of its springs can understand the peculiar nature of the Israeli woodland.

Many forest trees in Israel are evergreen and maintain their leafy cover the year-round; these include the common holm oak, lentisk, carob, laurel, buckthorn and Phillyrea (an evergreen privet). Others are deciduous and shed their leaves to stand denuded in winter. Thus the face of the woods changes from season to season.

In the green mass of summer, shades can be discerned. It is not difficult to distinguish between the light green of the deciduous oak (Quercus infectoria) and the dark green of the evergreen oak (Quercus calliprinos), the yellowish green of arbutus, the dark gray patches of Spanish broom bushes and the reddish budding of terebinth leaves.

In fall, the leaves of many trees turn: the storax and Judas tree yellow, Mt. Tabor oaks become brown and the Palestine terebinth is painted wonderful shades of copper and gold — as though to suggest the colorful leaf-turning of the autumn of the temperate north. Fruits also ripen and contribute their touches to the picture — red arbutus berries, black buckthorn fruit, brown acorns of oaks and red bunches of smilax fruit.

But the real festival is in the spring when the trees and bushes burst into bloom. Even before their leaves develop, the Judas tree is covered with a torch of reddish pink flowers and the wild pear with a flurry of white ones. Other trees, such as the storax and wild hawthorn, bloom at the same time as the fresh new leaves unfold. Even evergreens renew their foliage. In spring the creamy strawberry tree flowers hang down in panicles among shiny thick leaves; the rare arrowhead bears it white flowers.

More modest, but nevertheless important in the tangle of the woodlands are the many kinds of climbers which invariably accompany trees and shrubs. Here are wild asparagus and madder plants, and the Italian honeysuckle with its sprays of yellow and mauve flowers which spread a marvelous scent in the forest. All these, and many more, combine to form the inimitable wonder of the woodland spring.

A torch of red flowers in early spring, the Judas tree of Israel (52) is appropriately called "red bud" in North America.

The scent of Italian honeysuckle (54) in the
woodland announces the presence of its flowers
even before they are seen.

*A rather low tree, its reddish new leaflets mark
out the terebinth (53) in spring.*

54

*And (he) went after the man of God,
and found him sitting under a terebinth;
and he said to him, Art thou the man
of God that camest from Judah?
And he said, I am.*

I KINGS 13, 14

55 *Red bark, shiny leaves, creamy racemes of flowers in spring and red berries in fall, all make the oriental strawberry tree (55, 56) one of the loveliest trees of the forest.*

The white flowers of the Syrian pear (57, 58)
will ripen into tasty fruit.

*Usually a grayish bush, Spanish broom (59) blazes into
golden bloom in spring.*

SPRING ON MT. HERMON

Hermon — the wall of rock and snow rising up from among the foothills of the Golan and Galilee; inaccessible to us until June 1967, it was always there in the distance, tantalizing, inviting. Invisible, but palpably present, during the stormy days of winter or the sultry haze of summer, it reappears in astonishing propinquity on clear days between the rains. It is then that its snowy peak can be seen from very great distances.

What is the magic of the Hermon? First of all — the snow. Not a few flakes that dissolve with the first rays of the sun, but fields of white covering the peak and slopes for months on end. Then, there is the height which dwarfs the hills of Israel; in a word, a veritable mountain.

This combination of altitude and snow forms a natural world totally different from anything found in other parts of Israel. The snowy aspect of winter and the rocky crags of summer form, of course, the paramount impression. But now that the peak and part of the Hermon slopes are accessible, we have discovered a rich world of flowering plants. Among these alpine plants are those rounded tufty cushion plants set among the rock and snow drifts. Many varied plant species, such as the wild cherry and prickly thrift, take on the cushion appearance at heights over 1700 ft.

The calendar seems to be turned back on climbing the Hermon in June and July; the higher one gets, the earlier in the year it seems. At a time when the gold and brown colors of the summer reign in the plains below, up above we are greeted with greens and purples set among bands of shiny white snow; now the cushion plants thrive and stinging flower spikes, such as the mountain lily and the Lebanon eremurus, grow up among crevices and on the rocky plates. The many rock craters found on the mountain — erosion hollows which have been filled with a bed of alluvium — are the greatest joy. The snow persists longest in the craters, so that spring flowering arrives here when the mountain slopes already have taken on a summer aspect.

*Found only on the slopes of Hermon and in the
Golan, the Hermon iris (60) belongs to an
exclusive group of gorgeous irises growing only
in the Near East.*

61

As snows melt, flowers of bulbous plants appear
— thick-leaved fritillary (61) and a
multicolored tulip (62) resembling one found in
the Negev.

*Wild cherry (63) on the Hermon is a shrub, but
its flowers rival the Japanese cherry blossom.*

*Another two shrubby alpine plants are Lebanon rose (64) and
the cushiony prickly thrift (65).*

*The wilderness and the solitary place
shall be glad for them; and the desert
shall rejoice, and blossom as the rose.*

ISAIAH 35, 1

64

65

Pale iris (66) blooms only in the heights of Hermon, but mountain lilies (67) are also found in Negev wildernesses.

Climb high enough on rocky terraces and find Lebanon eremurus (68).

THORNS
AND THISTLES
OF SUMMER

With the summer comes the time of these prickly weeds. Not that they are absent the year round, but now they flourish, perhaps too much, for all to see and feel. The herbaceous plants that remained fresh until late spring have already wilted. Now the prickly plants are in full command and rise up high — even to the height of a man. Some, like the wild artichoke and globe thistle, are in full bloom; others, like the milk thistle, have already bloomed and their seeds are being spread.

It seems that these plants have scourged mankind ever since the first man was cursed — "in toil shall you eat of the ground... and thorns and thistles shall it bring forth to you, and you shall eat of the plants of the field." Even modern agriculture has not found adequate means to overcome these hardy weeds. Their vigorous growth, tremendous fruitfulness and highly effective means of seed dispersal make it possible for some of them to spread far and wide, while other thistles cleave stubbornly to fallow fields and waysides, driving out other forms of vegetation. Where did these thistles come from? Like other annuals, they first appear as modest green seedlings after the first rains. Even the perennials among them have an unassuming leafy aspect during the wet winter. When the summer heat has dried the ground and most of the herbs and grasses, then the soft large

*leaves of our thorns are discarded in favor of scaly
prickly stems which conserve their moisture and grow
up above the wilting landscape.*

*The advantage of blooming when most other plants
have long since died is obvious on approaching
clumps of thistles in flower. The buzzing, humming
sounds of the many insects busy at the flowers
indicate that the thistles now monopolize the
attention of these most important instruments of
cross-pollination.*

*If we are not taken aback by their scratchy and
prickly nature, the interesting forms of these
composites and their beautiful colors can be very
rewarding to the close observer.*

Stately acanthus (69) and its thorns.

Blue centaury (70) is a thistle.

Milk thistle (71) reaches giant stature in summer fields.

Thorns *also and* thistles *shall it bring forth to thee;* and thou shalt eat the herb of the field.

GENESIS 3, 18

For the earth which drinketh in the rain that cometh oft upon it, and bringeth forth herbs meet for them by whom it is dressed, receiveth blessing from God: But that which beareth thorns *and* briers *is rejected and is nigh unto cursing: whose end is to be burned.*

HEBREWS 6, 7–8

Globe thistle (72) bristles like a purplish hedgehog in the hot sunshine.

Wild artichoke (73) — loveliest of the thorny composites.

73

*For thus saith the Lord to the men of Judah and Jerusalem,
Break up your fallow ground, and sow not among* thorns.

JEREMIAH 4, 3

Distaff thistle (76) — tardiest of the thorny plants of summer.

FLOWERS OF SWAMP
AND SHORE

In July and August, only water plants and those of the seashore find respite from the parched days of summer to succeed in bringing forth their best flowers. The vacationer also seeking the cool beaches or the refreshing waters of lakes and streams, now encounters them.

During the many centuries when hill terraces were falling into ruin, when sand dunes encroached on the coastal plains and the woodlands were wantonly burnt down and overgrazed, the swamps spread over many parts of the country where streams grew stagnant for want of drainage. Here the frogs croaked and malaria mosquitos hummed; here, too, a wonderful array of aquatic plants thrived undisturbed. But the "good old days" are gone now that the swamps have been drained; only here and there, in ponds, yet-untapped streams and in nature preserves, can we find the special world of the swamp plants. Here plants from the temperate north, such as the bladderwort with its traps for capturing insects and the frogbit, met with the papyrus and marsilia fern from tropical Africa in convivial circumstances. With progressive draining, the bladderwort and marsilia, as well as some kinds of pond weeds and pond lily, have disappeared or are exceedingly rare. What remains is nevertheless enough to give us a good idea of life in the swamp.

Year-round observations of swamp vegetation seems to indicate a "topsy-turvy" world. In spring when hills and valleys are all in bloom, the swamp seems to be in a deep winter torpor — cold and gray with chilled moribund vegetation. In summer, when all about has dried, then the swamp plants burst into growth and flowers are seen: flowering rush, purple loosestrife, mosquito plant, Pulicaria, etc. It is the conservative heating quality of water that dictates this: not until the waters have been heated sufficiently from the winter chill is blooming possible.

The plants on the seashore, as well, wait through the cold stormy day of winter and spring before blooming. When the salty spray has subsided and the sea taken on a glassy surface, then the sea daffodil and evening primrose light up the sandstone cliffs of the coast.

Summer comes and oleander (77) colors stream
courses with vivid pink.

Arrow-shaped leaves of morning glory (78)
climb among the marsh tangle.

The marvelous blue lotus (80) fled when the
swamps were drained, but yellow pond lily (81)
still lingers on in ponds and lakelets.

Consider the lilies *how they grow: they toil
not, they spin not; and yet I say unto you,
that Solomon in all his glory was not
arrayed like one of these.*

LUKE 12, 27

The native willow herb (83) has always been
common and profuse in swampy places, while
its relative the evening primrose (82) arrived at
Israel's sandy shores only decades ago.

Closing the circle and opening the new season of flowers,
glorious sea lily (84) blazes out on the seacoast.

THE FLOWERS
IN THEIR SEASON

HARBINGERS OF THE RAINS

1. SEA SQUILL
Urginea maritima (L) Bak.
LILIACEAE. LILY FAMILY.

Blooms at the end of summer.
The sea squill is a perennial plant ranging, in Israel, from the north down to the central Negev. It has a thick subterranean bulb which yields a glucoside used, in some countries, for rat poison and insecticide. If we pull the bulb out in midsummer and keep it in shade, it will bloom out of the soil — as the inflorescence belongs to the previous blooming phase, the one in which nutrients were stored in the bulb. Its floral axis might reach the height of 1 m., the diameter of its flowers is about 1.5 cm. When the floral axis has reached its full length, the blooming begins, progressing from the base towards the tip. At morning, several flowers open at the base of the stem and wilt in the same evening; the next morning, upper flowers open and so forth, day after day. The blooming-span is from a week to ten days; the raceme may comprise up to 100 flowers. The broad leaves (up to 15 cm.) appear after the blooming is completed and wilt at the onset of next summer.

2. STERNBERGIA
Strenbergia clusiana Spreng.
(= Sternbergia spaffordiana Dinsm.)
AMARYLLIDACEAE. AMARYLLIS FAMILY.

Blooms in autumn. Grows on Mt. Meron, in the Judean hills and in some of the Negev hills.
The sternbergia is a perennial, bulbous plant. The bulb has thin brown sheathing leaves; it produces three to five flowers which open just above the ground. The floral tepals are 5–8 cm. long. The life-span of the flower is several days; its color changes from greenish yellow at the beginning to hot orange turning brownish at the end.
The ovary of the flower, which is subterranean during the blooming period, develops into a fleshy capsule carried on a short stalk; when ripe, the capsule splits open, scattering big, black seeds on which white corpuscle of fat tissue is conspicuous. It serves as a bait for ants, which thus help to better disperse the seeds.
The sternbergia leafs-out only after the rains; the leaves are narrow, strap-shaped and curled at the end. It is a protected wild-flower.

3. JERUSALEM MEADOW SAFFRON
Colchicum hierosolymitanum Feinbr.
LILIACEAE. LILY FAMILY

A perennial, tuberous plant growing in the fields and groves of the Judean hills, in the Galilee and the Golan. Blooms in autumn; the flowers always precede the leaves by a few weeks. The leaves are broader than those of Steven's meadow saffron (10). The flowers measure about 6.5 cm. in length.

4. AUTUMN SQUILL
Scilla autumnalis L.
LILIACEAE. LILY FAMILY.

Blooms in autumn, in sparse clusters, in the hills of the Mediterranean zone.
A perennial plant with a small bulb of about 2 cm. The floral axis measures about 15 cm. and each flower – 5 mm. The flowering, like that of the sea squill, "climbs up" the axis; but the flowers of the autumn squill live for several days.

5. BIARUM
Biarum bovei Blume
ARACEAE. AROID FAMILY.

Blooms in autumn, in batha and the cultivated and fallow fields of the Carmel and the Galilee. A perennial, tuberous plant. During its bloom we actually see the inflorescence, subtended by a prominent and brightly colored spathe, around a brown stalk of about 10 cm., called rachis.
The spathe has two distinct parts: the upper one resembles a showy flag and the lower is jar-shaped. That jar conceals two whorls of tiny flowers, arranged on the lower part of the rachis. The pistillate flowers grow in the upper row, above the staminate flowers; both kinds have no tepals. The two whorls are separated by a bristly wreath. The inflorescence opens in the afternoon; it has a fetid odor which attracts dung beetles and carrion flies. The insects crawl along the spathe and rachis and then slip into the jar. Once trapped inside, they cannot get out until the next day — when the staminate flowers open and scatter their pollen on the involuntary pollinators. By then the rachis will have lost its slipperiness and the insects will get out, all covered with pollen. However, they will soon be trapped in the jar of another biarum plant,

which has just opened its pistillate flowers: the pollen grains will rub off against the sticky stigmas. Thus the visiting insects help the cross-pollination of the biarum.

6. SMALL FLOWERED PANCRATIUM
Pancratium parviflorum Dec.
AMARYLLIDACEAE. AMARYLLIS FAMILY.

Blooms in autumn, in the rock crevices of the hilly regions and the sandstone cliffs of the coastal plain. The pancratium is a perennial plant with a thick bulb. The inflorescence is umbellate, subtended, before opening, by a whitish, membranous spathe. The flowers measure 3–4 cm.; they have a toothed corona, connecting the stamens, as typical of the genus.

The leaves come out approximately a month after the flowering; they are linear, with a bright longitudinal stripe. The seeds, like those of the sternbergia, have a fat corpuscle, serving as a bait for ants.

The small flowered pancratium is a protected wild-flower.

7. LATE-FLOWERING NARCISSUS
Narcissus serotinus L.
AMARYLLIDACEAE. AMARYLLIS FAMILY.

Found mostly in the sandstone hills of the Carmel coast.

Blooms in mid-autumn, about a month before the polyanthus narcissus. But that is not the only difference between the two related plants. The late-flowering narcissus has mostly a solitary flower and never more than two; its corona is small and modest and when the plant reaches (when 3–5 years old) the flowering stage it has no leaves at all. The polyanthus narcissus has an inflorescence of 10 flowers and more, rising out of green leaves and its corona is big and showy.

When the bloom is completed, the stem of the late-flowering narcissus does not stop growing; it fulfils the functions of assimilating and storing up the nutrients in the bulb.

8. SMILAX (GREENBRIER)
Smilax aspera L.
LILIACEAE. LILY FAMILY.

A climbing shrub, growing in woodland and rocky places. Whenever there is some support it twines around it, rising to the light; without support, it becomes a prostrate, thorny tangle.

The smilax blooms in spring. The plants are dioecious — the stamens and pistills are in separate flowers, on separate plants. The fruits (berries) ripen during the summer in dense bundles, acquiring dark-red color in autumn.

FLOWERS OF AUTUMN

9. (PHEASANT'S EYE NARCISSUS) POLYANTHUS NARCISSUS
Narcissus tazetta L.
AMARYLLIDACEAE. AMARYLLIS FAMILY.

A perennial, bulbous herb, flowering in autumn in most regions of the country. Some botanists believe it to be "the lily of the valley" mentioned in The Song of Solomon (2:1). In reality the narcissi, though found in hilly regions too, occur mostly in the valleys, where the soil is heavy and saturated with water. Important habitats of the narcissi were destroyed by the drainage of marshes in Israel.

The long, narrow leaves sprout after the first rains; two to three weeks later begins the flowering.

The umbellate inflorescence comprises ten and more flowers of about 3 cm. each; the floral axis is about 20–30 cm. high.

The narcissus' flowers, characterized by their strong scent, tend sideways and not upwards; this angle, in addition to the yellow, cup-like corona, prevents the stamens from getting wet. That might be the reason why the narcissus' flowers, unlike those of most autumnal plants, do not close at night or during rainfall.

The pheasant's eye — Polyanthus narcissus is a protected wild-flower.

10. STEVEN'S MEADOW SAFFRON
Colchicum steveni Kunth
LILIACEAE. LILY FAMILY.

Abounds in most regions of the country — apart from the Negev — immediately after the first rains.

A perennial herb with an annually regenerating tuber.

Unlike the Jerusalem meadow saffron, which blooms before leafing out, the Steven's meadow saffron flowers from among its narrow, green leaves.

The floral tepals measure 3–4 cm.

The tuber yields poisonous colchicine in accordance with the plant's scientific name.

11. WINTER CROCUS
Crocus hyemalis Boiss.
IRIDACEAE. IRIS FAMILY.

Blooms in autumn, in low-shrub formations in the north of the country. A perennial plant whose stem, like that of Steven's meadow saffron, is modified into an annually regenerating tuber. But whereas the regenerative bud of the saffron grows beside the old tuber, that of the crocus is produced above the tuber of yesteryear.

The floral tepals measure about 5 cm. in length.

The flower resembles that of the saffron in its appearance but it has three stamens — characteristic of the Iris family and, likewise, an inferior ovary — whereas the saffron has six stamens and a superior ovary.

The leaves have a vertical, silvery stripe.

The crocus may have various uses: the fragrant stamens help in the making of a spice, saffron, used for cooking and baking. In ancient times it served as a perfume when diluted in oil and was mentioned in The Song of Solomon as "spikenard and saffron" (4:14). Its golden stigmas were used for the dyeing of threads and hence probably its scientific name "Crocus", signifying "thread".

Nowadays the Arab shepherds roast the crocus' tubers and eat them.

12. CYCLAMEN, FLORISTS' CYCLAMEN
Cyclamen persicum Mill.
PRIMULACEAE. PRIMROSE FAMILY.

A perennial herb with a large corm, growing in rock crevices and shady places in the Mediterranean zone of Israel.

The cyclamen blooms from autumn to spring.

The flower stalks measure about 15 cm. and the flowers — about 3 cm.; they live for over a fortnight and their color gamut ranges from whitish to dark pink.

The spotting of the big, heart-shaped leaves also varies from plant to plant.

The specific shape of the cyclamen is due to its double bending: the flower stalk is bent down and the tepal lobes are rolled up into a sort of corona, elevated above a purplish opening. That arrangement prevents the wetting of the pollen.

This species is the origin/ancestor of the cultivated cyclamen, which is a popular ornamental.

The cyclamen is a protected wild-flower.

13. PALESTINE IRIS
Iris palaestina Boiss.
IRIDACEAE. IRIS FAMILY.

A perennial, bulbous plant, blooming at the beginning of winter, from the northern Negev to the Galilee.

Unlike most irises this is a low plant, growing in dense clusters. Its flowers measure 5–6 cm.

14. DAISY
Bellis silvestris Cyr.
COMPOSITAE. COMPOSITE FAMILY.

A perennial plant, with a thick rootstock. Blooms in the hilly low-shrub formations from the onset of rains until midwinter. The "flower" of the daisy is actually a many-flowered capitilum. The external whorl, whose white color at the beginning of the bloom turns later to pink, is composed of ligulate pistillate flowers, attracting insects.

With the fall of evening they bend down, thus shielding the yellow, tubular flowers in the center, and in which the seeds develop after pollination. The akenes are small, dispersed by winds.

The daisy is an ornamental plant, grown in gardens and pots.

15. JACK-IN-THE-PULPIT
Arisarum vulgare Targ.
ARACEAE. AROID FAMILY.

Was sometimes called "Aaron's wand."

A perennial herb, producing a corm or a rootstock. Grows in orchards, fallow fields and scrubland; blooms at the beginning of winter. The flowers of Jack-in-the-pulpit, like those of the biarum (4) are unisexual; they are arranged on the lower part of the rachis, whose tip protrudes above the spathe.

In winter, the small ovaries produce a raceme of swollen fruit.

In spring, the big leaves wilt and the rootstock remains underground.

FLOWERS OF SPRING

16. ALMOND
Amygdalus communis L.
ROSACEAE. ROSE FAMILY.

A low deciduous tree growing in plantations and groves, where it produces edible fruit. A wild ancestral variant of this species grows in woodlands in the north of the country; its fruit are bitter and inedible. Another species is the small-leaved almond, found on the slopes of the Jordan valley and in the Negev hills; its flowers are slightly more pink.

The almond tree is an early bloomer. It sheds its leaves in winter but flowers at the onset of spring, even before leafing out. That early bloom, characteristic of the almond, is conveyed in its Hebrew name: "shakèd", signifying "industrious", "diligent".

The almond has been growing in the Holy Land since ancient times and is often mentioned in the Bible. The almond rod was a sign of God's choice of Aaron and his sons for His servants: "... and, behold, the rod of Aaron of the house of Levi was budded, and brought forth buds, and bloomed blossoms and yielded almonds." (Numbers, 17:8). The branches of the golden candlestick were "made like unto almonds, with a knop and a flower in one branch" (Exodus, 25:33), and the prophet Jeremiah saw a rod of the almond tree as a symbol of God's haste to fulfil His Word.

17–18. POPPY ANEMONE
Anemone coronaria L.
RANUNCULACEAE. BUTTERCUP FAMILY.

The red anemone is a perennial plant, with a small, annually regenerating tuber. Its red blossom can be seen from the end of autumn till the spring.

The anemone does not have a fixed number of tepals; they vary from 5 to 12 in different flowers. The floral bud is cupped by three dissected leaflets which look like sepals but are really bracts; this becomes more evident when the pedicel elongates and the flower is separated from the bracts.

The flowers measure about 5 cm.; every flower lives for a few days, opening in the morning and closing at nightfall.

Besides the red anemone there can also be found pink, white and blue varieties. Those occur mainly in the hilly regions of the north, down to the central part of Israel.

19. DARK-PURPLE IRIS
Iris atropurpurea Bak.
IRIDACEAE. IRIS FAMILY.

A perennial plant, producing thin, horizontal rhizomes. Grows in big clusters, which sometimes comprise over 100 specimens. Can be found in the sandy soil and sandstone hills of southern and central coastal plain. Blooms in early spring.

The flower stalk might reach the height of 40 cm. and the flowers measure about 9 cm. in diameter. Their color varies from yellowish-brown to red-brown and even black. The dark-purple iris belongs to a special division within the genus Iris, called Oncocyclus, which includes 40 species; ten of them are endemic. One characteristic of the Oncocyclus is that the floral axis carries a single flower, cupped by vertical, hirsute tepals.

The iris grows in the midst of the most densely populated area in Israel; its growth was, therefore, greatly damaged. Nowadays the dark-purple iris is a protected wild-flower.

20. TEL-AVIV GARLIC
Allium tel-avivense Eig.
ROSACEAE. ROSE FAMILY.

A perennial, bulbous plant. Blooms in winter, in the light soils and the sandstone hills of the coastal plains, the Sharon and Acre valley. The floral axis might reach the height of 40 cm., but it is more often about 25 cm.; the inflorescence measures about 12 cm. in diameter. The Tel-Aviv garlic is one of 250 endemic species of Israel, i.e. — species whose distribution is limited to our country only.

21. THE LESSER CROWFOOT
Ranunculus ficaria L.
RANUNCULACEAE. BUTTERCUP FAMILY.

A perennial plant with a leaf rosette close to the ground. Blooms in spring in the heavy, moist soils of the Judean hills, on Mt. Carmel, in the Galilee and in the Golan; occurs mainly in the shade of olive groves. The yellow, shiny flowers measure 4 cm. in diameter; they are probably pollinated by flies.

The lesser crowfoot has a tuft of thick roots, serving for storage of nutrients.

22. ROUND-LEAVED CYCLAMEN
Cyclamen coum Mill.
PRIMULACEAE. PRIMROSE FAMILY.

A perennial herb, with a small corm. Blooms in early spring on Mt. Meron, in the north of the Golan and on Mt. Hermon.
The round-leaved cyclamen occurs in several Mediterranean countries.
It requires a considerable degree of cold and a great amount of precipitation.
The floral stalk measures about 5 cm. and the small flowers — only 1 cm.
The round-leaved cyclamen differs from the common cyclamen in the size of flowers, their color and in the size and shape of its leaves.
It is a protected wild-flower.

23. KING'S SPEAR, ASPHODEL, JACOB'S-ROD
Asphodeline lutea (L.) Rchb.
LILIACEAE. LILY FAMILY.

A perennial plant, with a tuft of thick roots. Blooms in March, in moist places from the Negev to the Galilee.
The floral axis approaches 1 m. and bears numerous flowers: at the tip, the closed floral buds; underneath, spreading the open flowers, each measuring about 5.5 cm., with six petals of different colors and shapes; at the base, the ripening round capsules.
The king's spear is a protected wild-flower.

24. MOUNTAIN LUPINE
Lupinus pilosus Murr.
FABACEAE.

An annual herb. Blooms in March, in the heavy soils of the Judean hills, Samaria, on Mt. Carmel and in the Galilee and the Golan.
The plant is 35–40 cm. high; the flowers measure about 2 cm.
All parts of the plant are covered with felt, which retains the rain and dew drops. The leaves are dissected into 10 long leaflets, or less, which fold in the evening and unfold in the morning.
The lupine is bitter and poisonous and most animals avoid it. The flower produces hirsute legumes in which there are 3–6 seeds.
In ancient times people used to sweeten the seeds by soaking them in boiling water, to remove the bitter taste. Nowadays, Arab pedlars sometimes sell cooked and salted lupine seeds of another species. The blue lupine is a protected wild-flower.

25. PURPLE GRAPE HYACINTH
Muscari comosum (L.) Mill.
(= Leopoldia comosa (L.) Parl.)
LILIACEAE. LILY FAMILY

A perennial, bulbous plant. Blooms in March and April mainly in fields in the coastal plain.
The floral axis reaches the height of 25 cm; the fertile flowers measure only 8 mm.
At the top of the inflorescence there is a cluster of purple flowers, devoid of stamens and pistils.
They are sterile but showy, destined to attract insects to pollinate the tiny, fertile flowers underneath.
The purple grape hyacinth may be recognized not only by its blossom but also by its three leaves, which are red at the base, due to the red pigment anthocyanin.

26. HYACINTH SQUILL
Scilla hyacinthoides L.
LILIACEAE. LILY FAMILY.

A perennial plant, with a thick bulb. Blooms from February to April in the low-shrub formations and woodland of the Mediterranean zone.
The floral axis reaches the height of 1 m.
It carries numerous flowers, borne on long pedicels and measuring about 1 cm. each.
The flowering, like that of the sea squill (1), begins at the base of the raceme and gradually progresses towards the top; but it is not as orderly as that of the sea squill.

27. SHARON TULIP
Tulipa sharonensis Dinsm.
LILIACEAE. LILY FAMILY.

A perennial, bulbous plant. Blooms in March-April, in the light soils and the sandstone hills of the coastal plain.
The average height of the floral stalk is 10–15 cm. but it might even reach 35 cm.; the flowers measure 3.5–5 cm.
The bulb of the tulip lies 25–30 cm. under the ground surface. The bulb grows downwards for about three years; the plant blooms only four years after germinating from seed. Every bulb annually produces a single floral stalk, carrying a solitary flower.
The Sharon tulip, like all other species of this genus, is a protected wild-flower.

28. COMMON CHRYSANTHEMUM
Chrysanthemum coronarium L.
COMPOSITAE. COMPOSITE FAMILY.

An annual herb. Blooms in profusion in spring, in fallow fields, grazing-grounds and waysides all over the country. The plants might reach the height of 70 cm. and more; the width of the capitulum is about 5 cm.
The chrysanthemum abounds mainly in deserted places, among dung and ruins, where there is a profusion of nitrogen in the soil. In such places the plants grow densely and stifle the germination of any other plant in their midst.
The Arab peasant-women collect the fragrant dissected leaves of the chrysanthemum and use them to spice vegetable salads.

29. SPRING GROUNDSEL
Senecio vernalis Wald. & Kit..
COMPOSITAE. COMPOSITE FAMILY.

An annual herb, found in profusion in most regions of the country. The blooming-span is relatively long: from the end of December, in the light soils of the Coastal Plain, to April, when it still flowers in the heavy soils of the hills.
The capitulum bears ligulate flowers, surrounding the tubular flowers in the center. The ligulate flowers recurve with the fall of evening. The ripening akenes have tufts of woolly hairs and the akene carrying capitula resemble white-haired heads. This accounts for the Hebrew name of the groundsel: "savyon", signifying "grandfatherly".

30. PALESTINE MARIGOLD
Calendula palaestina Boiss.
COMPOSITAE. COMPOSITE FAMILY.

A low annual herb, found in fallow fields and low-shrub formations in most regions of the country. Blooms from January to April.
The capitulum is about 1.5 cm. wide. In the center there are reddish tubular flowers, having stamens and a degenerated pistil; they are sterile. The circumferential flowers are ligulate and fertile; together with the green tepals they shield the capitulum in the evening and during rainy days. During the day, the capitulum follows the course of the sun — like the sunflower.
The marginal flowers produce akenes, which bend towards the center and are endowed with a bill, resembling the cat's claw. Hence, the Hebrew name of the marigold, "tziporen khatul", i.e.,: "cat's claw".

31. PROLIFIC SCABIOUS
Scabiosa prolifera L.
DIPSACEAE. TEASEL FAMILY.

An annual plant. Blooms from February till May, in fallow fields and low-shrub formations in the central and northern regions of the country.
At first sight the inflorescence of the scabious looks as if it belongs to the Composite Family. The difference becomes more evident after the bloom; each flower of the scabious has two goblets, one within the other. When the petals wither, the external calyx keeps growing and turns into a membranous corona, which helps the dispersal of the fruits. This corona is characteristic of the genus.

32. JERUSALEM SAGE
Salvia hierosolymitana Boiss.
LABIATAE. MINT FAMILY.

A perennial plant. Blooms from March to June in the batha in the center and north of the country.
The stem grows out of a prostrate leaf-rosette; it is about 80 cm. high.
The flowers measure about 3 cm.
Unlike the other 20 species of the sage genus found in Israel, the Jerusalem sage is scentless.

33. ANATOLIAN ORCHID
Orchis anatolica Boiss.
ORCHIDACEAE. ORCHID FAMILY

A perennial, tuberous plant, common in the batha, garigue and woodland of the northern regions. Blooms in March and April.
The floral axis is 20 cm. high and the flowers measure 3 cm., from the edge of the labellum to the edge of the spur.
When not in blossom, it can be recognized by the brown spots on its leaves.
Like the other 30 species of this family growing in Israel, the Anatolian orchid is a protected wild-flower.

34. VIPER'S BUGLOSS
Echium angustifolium Mill.
BORAGINACEAE. BORAGE FAMILY.

A perennial plant with stems often prostrate on the ground. Blooms from March till June, in low shrub formation and fallow fields all over the country.
Its flowers measure about 1.5 cm. They are pink at the beginning of flowering, but gradually turn blue-violet. The pistil is forked at the end, resembling a snake's

tongue, hence probably the generic name "viper's bugloss." The stems and leaves of the bugloss are covered with bristles, characteristic of most of the Borage Family.

35. RED CORN POPPY, CARMEL POPPY
Papaver carmeli Feinbr.
PAPAVERACEAE. POPPY FAMILY.

An annual herb, common on roadsides and in cultivated fields in the north. Starts blooming in March but abounds mostly in April, when the other red wildflowers have already wilted. The plant is 40–50 cm. high and the flowers measure about 5 cm.

The floral buds are bent down and enclosed by two green sepals. With the beginning of the blossom, the pedicel straightens, the sepals are shed and the four crumpled petals stretch and unfold.

The number of petals may help us distinguish the poppy from the anemone and the crowfoot. The crowfoot has five petals. whereas the anemone, though its petals vary in number, never has less than five. The stems and leaves of the poppy are bristly; it yields a poisonous yellow sap and a repulsive odor. These might be the plant's means of defense against cattle. That is also the reason why some botanists identify the poppy with the poisonous hemlock often mentioned in the Bible.

36. ALEPPO HORNED POPPY
Gluacium aleppicum Boiss. & Hausskn.
PAPAVERACEAE. POPPY FAMILY.

A perennial plant. Blooms in April and May in the northern Galilee and near Lake Tiberias. The flowers measure about 7 cm.

The Aleppo horned poppy is quite similar to the red corn poppy (35). The differences become more evident during the ripening of the fruits. The red corn poppy has a disk-shaped stigma, with many lobes; its ovary develops into an oval capsule. The Aleppo horned poppy has a stigma of two lobes only, and the fruit is elongated, linear and narrow.

37. ORIENTAL CROWFOOT
Ranunculus millefolius Banks et Sol.
RANUNCULACEAE. BUTTERCUP FAMILY.

A perennial plant with a tuft of thick roots. Blooms in spring, in the central and northern scrublands as well as in the southern steppes.

The floral axis is 20 cm. high and the flowers measure about 2 cm. They are yellow and shiny as if coated with lacquer.

The stems and the cleft leaves are covered with greyish, thick hairs, which distinguish the oriental crowfoot from other species of this genus.

38. MICHAUXIA
Michauxia campanuloides L'Her.
CAMPANULACEAE. BELLFLOWER FAMILY.

A perennial herb, growing in loose, calcerous soil in the northern Galilee.

During the winter, the Michauxia has just a rosette of leaves close to the ground. The floral stalk starts growing at the beginning of spring and reaches the height of 1.5 m. The blossom begins in May. The flowers have a protruding pistil and measure about 7 cm.

39. LARGE OR COMMON SNAPDRAGON
Antirrhunum majus L.
SCROPHULARIACEAE. FIGWORT FAMILY.

A perennial plant. Grows in calcerous soils or rocky walls in the northern Galilee. Found frequently in the vicinity of the Michauxia (38).

The large snapdragon blooms all year round, but its pink blossom is most profuse in May. The flowers measure about 3.5 cm. The colors of the wild snapdragon range from white to pink; the cultivated derived from this species have a much richer range of colors.

40. LORTET IRIS
Iris lorteti Barb.
IRIDACEAE. IRIS FAMILY.

A perennial herb, with a rhizome. The only place in the world where it grows is north-eastern Galilee. Blooms in May. The big, gorgeous flowers measure 11 cm. and the floral stalks might reach 40 cm.

The Lortet iris requires specific ecological conditions; when transferred into gardens and nurseries, it soon wilts. It is a protected wild-flower.

41. MADONNA LILY
Lilium candidum L.
LILIACEAE. LILY FAMILY.

A perennial, bulbous herb, very rare in Israel. Grows on cliffs and in rock crevices in a few places on the

Carmel and in the Galilee. In spring, a stem rises out of a leaf rosette reaching 1.5 m. in height; it is leafy from its base up to the tip where the flowers are borne. The white, fragrant flowers blossom in May; they measure 8 cm. The Madonna lily is associated with the lily mentioned in The Song of Solomon; it is also related to the Christian tradition, and many lily bulbs were uprooted in the Middle Ages and transferred to monasteries in Europe. It is a protected wild-flower.

42. BRISTLY HOLLYHOCK
Althaea setosa Boiss.
MALVACEAE. MALLOW FAMILY.

A perennial herb. Blooms in the hills of the central and northern regions, at the time of barley harvest (June). The floral axis is 2 m. high and over and the flowers measure about 8 cm. in diameter. Some parts of the hollyhock are edible. Its cultivated varieties are colorful ornamentals.

SPRING IN THE NEGEV

43. WHITE BROOM
Retama raetam Webb
FABACEAE.

A shrub growing in the sands and wadis of the Negev, in the sandstone hills of the coastal plain and in rocky places in eastern Samaria. Reaches the height of 2 m. and more.
From February to March, the long, slender branches are covered with a blossom of small (1 cm.) white flowers.
At such times, the white broom is very showy — especially in the desert. But there are years when the broom does not flower at all; it stands, flowerless and greyish, in a sort of dormancy.
Most of the year the broom is leafless; only in winter does it sprout tiny leaves at the tips of its branches. The leaves are soon shed and the green branches fulfil the function of assimilation.
In ancient times, the roots of the broom were used as embers for fire.

44. PURPLE CORN FLAG
Gladiolus aleppicus Boiss.
IRIDACEAE. IRIS FAMILY.

A perennial, tuberous plant. Grows in corn fields in the Judean desert, Samaria and the Negev; abounds mostly in Arad valley. Blooms in March. Its flowers measure about 4 cm.
The purple corn flag should be distinguished from the pink corn flag, which is a different species common in grain fields, and from the gladiolus, which is a related cultivated ornamental.

45. MARY'S IRIS, HELEN'S IRIS
Iris helenae Barb.
(= Iris mariae Barb.)
IRIDACEAE. IRIS FAMILY.

A perennial plant, with rhizomes, confined only to the sands of the western and northern Negev, blooming in March. This is another member of endemic group of species of the Oncocyclus subgenus; but it is the smallest among them, with flowers about 9 cm. in diameter.
Mary's iris is a protected wild-flower.

46. DESERT BROOMRAPE
Cistanche tubulosa Wright
OROBANCHACEAE. BROOMRAPE FAMILY.

A perennial, parasitic plant, living on the roots of the broom, the tamarisk, the saltbush and other plants. Grows in the wadis of the Negev and the Arava. The broomrape is underground most of the time, sucking its sustenance from the roots of its host-plant.
Blooms in March-April, when a fleshy stem bursts out of the ground with a great force. The floral buds are arranged as if on a spike; the flowers measure about 4 cm. After the flowering and the seed dispersal the stem blackens and breaks and the plant continues its existence underground.

47. LION'S LEAF
Leontice leontopetalum L.
BERBERIDACEAE. BARBERRY FAMILY.

A perennial plant, with a tuber deep under the surface of ground. Grows in all parts of the country, but mainly in the loess soils of the northern Negev.

Starts blooming in mid-January in the Negev and in the north still flowering in April. The flowers measure about 2 cm. The fertilized ovaries develop into bladder-like, membranous fruits.

The seeds are dispersed by wind; with the onset of summer, the stems break at the base and the wind carries and rolls it in the fields; the vesicular fruits then split open and release the seeds.

48. HIRSUTE STORK'S BILL
Erodium hirtum (Forssk.) Willd.
GERANIACEAE. GERANIUM FAMILY.

A perennial herb. Blooms in March-April in the Negev and the Judean desert.

In the summer and in years of drought, the branches of the stork's bill become dry and seem lifeless; but they come alive with the first rains, then bloom.

49. SUN ROSE
Helianthemum vesicarium Boiss.
CISTACEAE. ROCKROSE FAMILY.

A low shrub, growing on the rocky slopes of the Negev and the Judean desert. Flowers from February to April, according to the rains. Has a multi-colored blossom — violet, pink, purplish. The flowers measure about 2.5 cm. in diameter.

In rainy years, the sun rose and the stork's bill color the desert with the profusion of their blossom.

50. ROSE DOCK, CYPRUS SORREL
Rumex cyprius Murb.
POLYGONACEAE. BUCKWHEAT FAMILY

An annual herb, grows mainly in the Negev steppes and the Judean desert. The greenish flowers are small and inconspicuous but after the pollination, three out of the six tepals keep growing, and gradually turn pink-red. They enclose the ripening fruit which measures, with the enclosing leaves, about 1.5 cm. Thus the showy, pinkish racemes are not of flowers but of fruits. The rose dock also has juicy, tasty sour leaves, eaten with relish by the shepherds.

51. SODOM APPLE
Calotropis procera R. Br.
ASCLEPIDACEAE. MILKWEED FAMILY.

A poisonous shrub growing in oases, mainly in Ein-Gedi and the Jordan Valley.

Blooms in spring and summer.

The shrub is 2 m. high: the flowers measure about 2 cm. in diameter. They produce round, swollen fruits about 10 cm., which gave the plant its popular name "Sodom apple". The branches and leaves (particularly below) are covered with thick felt, once collected and used by local Arabs for setting fire with a flintstone. The seeds are endowed with silky tufts, filling the fruit.

The Sodom apple is one of the tropical plants growing in Israel.

WOODLAND FLOWERS

52. JUDAS TREE OF ISRAEL
Cercis siliquastrum L.
CAESALPINIACEAE. CAESALPINIA FAMILY.

A deciduous tree, growing in humid mesophyllic woodlands in the Galilee and the Carmel, as well as in several places in Samaria and the Judean hills. Might reach the height of 6–7 m.

The tree sheds its leaves in winter. In March–April, even before the branches sprout leaves, the budding begins. The tree becomes covered with thousands of floral buds, growing in tiny racemes. The buds soon open and the tree is clothed in a gorgeous pink blossom. The flowers measure about 1.5 cm. and the Arabs used to eat them because of their juiciness. The Judas tree is related to the Christian tradition. To

prevent the breaking of its attractive branches in blossom, it was declared a protected wild-tree. it It is also cultivated as ornamental.

53. TEREBINTH
Pistacia palaestina Boiss.
ANACARDIACEAE. SUMAC FAMILY.

A shrub or low tree, 3–4 m. high, usually accompanying the common oak. In autumn, the leaves turn yellow or red, before they are shed in winter. But there sometimes remain, at the tips of the branches, big, banana-shaped gallnuts. New, reddish leaflets reappear in spring, just before the beginning of the blossom in March-April. The flowers are inconspicuous, arranged in crowded racemes. The plants are dioecious — staminate or pistillate flowers growing on different trees. The pollination is accomplished by the wind. In Israel there also grows another species, the Atlantic terebinth, which is a more imposing tree. It was probably the Atlantic terebinth to which the translated (!) Bible often refers as an oak: "... and Jacob hid them under the oak which was by Shechem." (Genesis, 35:4); "the oak which was in Ophrah" (Judges, 6:11) and "every thick oak" in Ezekiel, 6:13, where the people of Israel worshipped idols.

The fruits of both species have been eaten, when roasted, by the locals. They differ from the fruits of the True Pistacia, P. vera (Pistachio tree) but the latter can be grafted on the Atlantic pistacia.

54. ITALIAN HONEYSUCKLE
Lonicera etrusca Santi
CAPRIFOLIACEAE. HONEYSUCKLE FAMILY.

A woody climber, growing in forests in the central and northern parts of the country. Might reach the height of 4–5 m.

Blooms in April and May. The flowers measure about 3 cm. and are white when young but gradually turn creamy.

The intoxicating scent of the honeysuckle attracts the night insects, which suck the flowers' nectar with their long proboscis.

The cultivated honeysuckle, grown in gardens, is a different species.

55–56. ORIENTAL STRAWBERRY TREE
Arbutus andrachne L.
ERICACEAE. HEATH FAMILY.

An evergreen tree growing in the Mediterranean woodland. Reaches the height of 4–5 m. Blooms in March-April in creamy panicles of small, less than 1 cm., flowers.

In autumn it ripens red, berry-like fruits, which are edible.

The strawberry tree is very showy because of its red dark, shiny leaves and creamy sprays of blossom. However, it is not cultivated because of its specific ecological requirements and slow growth-rate.

57–58. SYRIAN PEAR
Pyrus syriaca Boiss.
ROSACEAE. ROSE FAMILY.

A tree growing in the woods of Galilee, the Carmel, Samaria and Judea. Reaches the height of 6–7 m.

Sheds its leaves in winter. Like the almond, the Syrian pear also blooms before sprouting leaf, in April. The white flowers measure about 1.5 cm. in diameter. The fruits ripen in July, and are edible, for a short period of time.

59. SPANISH BUSH, WEAVER BROOM
Spartium junceum L.
FABACEAE.

A shrub growing in the woods of Galilee, the Carmel and the Judean hills.

Like the white broom (43), the Spanish bush is also leafless most of the year; it then resembles a grayish tangle, of about 3 m. But at the onset of spring it blazes into a golden blossom of flowers, about 3 cm. each.

The Spanish bush has long, slender twigs, which fulfil the function of photosynthesis.

The twigs, which serve for the making of nets and baskets, gave the plant its name, "spartium", signifying: rope (in Greek).

*SPRING ON MT. HERMON**

60. HERMON IRIS
Iris hermona Dinsm.
IRIDACEAE. IRIS FAMILY.

A perennial herb with a rhizome. Grows in the basalt plateaus of northern Golan and on the eastern slopes of the Hermon.

Flowers in April–May.

The floral axis reaches the height of 60 cm. and the large flowers measure about 13 cm. in diameter. The

* The identification of and the information on many Hermon plants are not final. Their description should therefore be approached with reserve.

Hermon iris resembles the Nazarene iris in its colors, but because of the differences between the two — the Hermon iris is bigger and less spotted — they are defined as two different species.

61. THICK-LEAVED FRITILLARY
Fritillaria crassifolia Boiss. et Huet
LILIACEAE. LILY FAMILY.

A perennial, bulbous plant. Grows in the heights of Mt. Hermon (from 1300 m. upwards) in rocky places and shade of shrubs. Blooms in April-May.
Unlike the two other species of fritillary found in Israel, the thick-leaved fritillary produces only one or two flowers; they measure about 1.5 cm.

62. MULTICOLORED LOWNE TULIP
Tulipa lownei Baker
LILIACEAE. LILY FAMILY.

A perennial, bulbous herb, growing on the high slopes of Mt. Hermon. Each plant produces a few flowers, of about 3 cm. In spite of its resemblance to the multicolored tulip found in the Negev hills, the two are different species.

63. WILD CHERRY
Cerasus prostrata (Lab.) Ser.
ROSACEAE. ROSE FAMILY.

A prostrate shrub. Grows in rocky ground, at heights over 1500 m. Blooms in April-May. The flowers measure about 1 cm. in diameter and attract attention in their pink blossom. In summer it sets small, dark-red drupes which, though sour and having large stones, are edible and tasty.

64. LEBANON ROSE
Rosa pulverulenta M. Bieb.
(= Rosa glutinosa Sibth. et Smith)
ROSACEAE. ROSE FAMILY.

A thorny shrub of about 50 cm., growing at heights over 1500 m. Blooms in May and June, the flowers measure about 3 cm. The red fruits ripen in summer and are edible. The leaves are covered with sticky glands. The fruit is prickly.

65. LEBANON PRICKLY THRIFT
Acantholimon libanoticum Boiss.
PLUMBAGINACEAE. LEADWORT FAMILY.

A cushion-like shrublet, growing at heights over 1700 m. In April-May, the blossom time, the grayish cushion becomes covered with the small, pink flowers. These are soon shed, but their whitish membranous calices (about 8 mm. in diameter each) remain on the stems for a long time.

66. PALE IRIS
Iris pallida Lam.
IRIDACEAE. IRIS FAMILY.

A perennial plant with creeping rhizomes. Grows in some wadis of the Hermon. Its floral axes are about 80 cm. high and bear 1–3 flowers of 9 cm. in diameter each.
The pale iris resembles the Mesopotamic iris, originated in southern Turkey and is common in Israel as a cultivated ornamental, mainly in Moslem cemeteries.

67. MOUNTAIN LILY, SIBERIAN LILY
Ixiolirion tataricum (Pall.) Hert.
(= Ixiolirion montanum Herb.)
AMARYLLIDACEAE. AMARYLLIS FAMILY.

A perennial, bulbous plant, growing on the slopes of Mt. Hermon, at heights over 1500 m. The flowers measure about 4 cm.
Apart from the Hermon, the mountain lily grows sporadically also in scrubland and fields of the Shefela, the Judean hills and the Carmel, as well as in certain habitats in the Negev and the Judean desert. It is a protected wild-flower.

68. LEBANON DESERT CANDLE (EREMURUS)
Eremurus spectabilis M. Bieb.
(= Eremurus libanoticus Boiss. et Bal.)
LILIACEAE. LILY FAMILY.

A perennial plant, with a tuft of thick roots, resembling the king's spear (23) or the Asphodel. Grows on the Hermon at heights over 1800 m. The floral axis is about 1 m. high, spadix-like, bearing along numerous flowers measuring 1–2 cm.

THORNS AND THISTLES OF SUMMER

69. ACANTHUS, SYRIAN BEARS BREECH
Acanthus syriacus Boiss.
ACANTHACEAE. ACANTHUS FAMILY.

A perennial herb, growing in fields and low-shrub formations in the central and northern parts of the country. Its 2-lipped, white flowers blossom in April-May, enclosed by violet, thorny bracts, along a thick floral axis. "Acanthus leaves" was a traditional ornamental pattern in Roman and Byzantine construction.

70. PINK CENTAURY
Centaurea crocodylium L.
COMPOSITAE. COMPOSITE FAMILY.

An annual herb. Grows in fields and batha mainly in the northern Galilee, where it is sometimes found in thick clusters.
The plant measures about 40 cm. in height and the heads — about 4 cm. in diameter. After the seeds are dispersed, its white and shiny receptacles attract the eye.

71. MILK THISTLE
Silybum marianum (L.) Gaertn.
COMPOSITAE. COMPOSITE FAMILY.

An annual herb, abounding on roadsides and in fallow fields all over the country.
Its growth begins with two small, round cotyledons that germinate after the first rains. Later on, a thorny, broad leaf-rosette, white-spotted, is produced. The stem will rise only in late spring; it might reach the stature of 1.5 m. and more. Thus the milky thistles sometimes form an impenetrable wall at the field edges. All the flowers of the thistle are tubular. They are usually violet or sometimes, white. The leaves of the thistle are relished by all creatures of the field and its achenes — by birds.

72. GLOBE THISTLE
Echinops adenocaulon Boiss.
COMPOSITAE. COMPOSITE FAMILY.

A perennial plant, found in scrublands and fallow fields in all parts of the country. Reaches the height of man; its heads measure about 7 cm. in diameter.
Each inflorescence is composed of numerous capitula, each of which contain one flower. Every flower has a 5-lobed corolla and an involucre composed of several whorls. The inner whorls are of elongated scales or thorns, protruding out of the head.
The head disintegrates in summer and its parts are dispersed by the wind.

73. WILD ARTICHOKE
Cynara syriaca Boiss.
COMPOSITAE. COMPOSITE FAMILY.

A perennial herb. Grows in heavy soils in valleys, in the lower Galilee and the Golan. The stem might reach the height of 1 m. and the capitulum — about 6 cm. in diameter.
The artichoke we eat is the cultivated derived species. Its edible parts are, after cooking, the base of the floral bracts and the receptacle.

74. COTTON THISTLE
Onopordon cynarocephalum Boiss. et Bl.
COMPOSITAE. COMPOSITE FAMILY.

A perennial herb, growing in waste and fallow fields. Its prickly winged stem reaches the height of 1.5 m.; the capitula measure about 4–6 cm. in diameter. Blooms in June, July and August.

75. CARLINE THISTLE
Carlina involucrata Poir.
COMPOSITAE. COMPOSITE FAMILY

A perennial herb, growing in rocky low-shrub formations in the Judean hills, Samaria, the Carmel and the Galilee. The thistle is about 0.5 m. in height and the capitulum measures 9 cm. in diameter.
Blooms from midsummer to autumn.

76. DISTAFF THISTLE
Atractylis comosa Sieb.
COMPOSITAE. COMPOSITE FAMILY.

A perennial herb, growing in rocky places of the hills. Is about 40 cm. high and the flowering heads measure 5 cm.
Blooms in midsummer and autumn and its mauve-violet flowers are the tardiest blossom of the dry season.
The achenes are endowed with long, woolly tufts, which make the heads look white in autumn.

FLOWERS OF SWAMP AND SHORE

77. OLEANDER
Nerium oleander L.
APOCYNACEAE. DOGBANE FAMILY.

An evergreen shrub; might reach the height of 3 m. Grows along streamcourses in the Jordan Valley and along the Jordan affluents, in the Hula valley, the Carmel, the Galilee and the Golan.

The stems and stiff leaves yield a milky sap, which is bitter and poisonous and therefore prevents most animals from feeding on the oleander.

It blossoms from April to midsummer; the flowers measure about 4 cm. in diameter and are very fragrant, particularly towards evening.

The oleander is widely cultivated as an ornamental. The cultivated strains sometimes have more than five petals, which is the natural number in the wild oleander flower.

78. MORNING GLORY
Ipomoea sagittata Poir.
CONVOLVULACEAE. MORNING GLORY FAMILY.

A perennial, twining herb, quite rare. Grows in the marshes of the Sharon and Acre valley.

Blooms during the summer; its flowers measure about 8 cm.

The leaves are arrow-shaped.

Two other species of the morning glory are grown in Israel as ornamentals. Another species of this genus, Ipomea batatas — the sweet potato — originated in tropical America and is an important tropical root-crop.

79. FLOWERING RUSH
Butomus ubellatus L.
BUTOMACEAE. BUTOMUS FAMILY.

A perennial plant with a horizontal rhizome. Grows in the marshes of the Sharon and the Hula valley and in the streams of the Golan.

Its narrow, erect leaves start sprouting at the onset of spring, followed by the floral axis, which might reach the height of over 80 cm.

Its umbels start flowering in April in the Sharon and are still in blossom in August, in the Golan. It is a protected wild-flower.

80. BLUE LOTUS
Nymphaea caerulea Sav.
NYMPHAEACEAE. WATERLILY FAMILY.

A perennial aquatic plant, growing in the ponds and streams of the Sharon and Acre valley. Blooms from spring to autumn. Its blue flowers rise out of the big leaves, whose petioles float on water. The flowers measure about 9 cm. in diameter.

The drainage of marshes has extinguished almost completely the growth of the blue lotus; rare specimens can still be found in the sources of the Yarkon, in the Afek affluents (Acre valley).

The lotus originated in the tropics and Israel is the northern boundary of its natural distribution.

It is a protected wild-flower.

81. YELLOW POND LILY
Nuphar luteum (L.) Sm.
NYMPHAEACEAE. WATERLILY FAMILY.

An aquatic perennial herb with a rhizome. Grows in the lakes, slow-flowing rivers and ponds of the Sharon, Acre valley and the Hula valley.

The flowers, which blossom in spring and summer, measure about 4 cm. in diameter. The many petals have been reduced and modified into nectaries and the yellow, showy leaves are the sepals.

Unlike the blue lotus and the white lotus, which are almost entirely extinguished, the yellow pond lily is still found in several places, mainly in the Yarkon river, the Taninim river and the Hula reserve.

82. DRUMMOND'S EVENING PRIMROSE
Oenthera drummondii Hook.
ONAGRACEAE. EVENING PRIMROSE FAMILY.

A perennial plant growing on the sands of the seashore. Originated in America and was brought to Israel only at the turn of the century, but nowadays abounds along the seacoast.

The evening primrose blooms during all summer; the flowers measure about 7 cm. in diameter. The evening primrose enables us to follow the cycle of flowering. At the beginning, the floral buds protrude over the branches. With the fall of evening, one of the four seams connecting the sepals breaks and shows the yellow stripe of the corolla. The sepals are gradually lowered as the corolla starts to stand out; then, in a sudden movement, the sepals curve backwards and the released petals spread and open. If we stay the night near the primrose, we will be able to observe the big moths, attracted by its abundance of nectar.

83. NATIVE WILLOWHERB
Epilobium hirsutum L.
ONAGRACEAE. EVENING PRIMROSE FAMILY.

A perennial herb, growing in moist places in the northern and central parts of the country.
Its leaves, fruits, and pedicels are covered with thick hairs. Might reach the height of 2 m. and its flowers measure about 2 cm. in diameter. Blooms in summer. After the bloom, is covered with the hair-tufts of the seeds.

84. SEA LILY
Pancratium maritimum L.
AMARYLLIDACEAE. AMARYLLIS FAMILY.

A perennial, bulbous plant, growing in the sands and sandstone hills along the seashore. The flowers of the sea lily, like those of several other plants growing along the coast, open only in the evening, as a protective measure against the salty spray blown by wind during the day. The big flowers measure about 9 cm. in diameter. The flower has a corona, like the narcissus, but as appendages of the stamens and not of the corolla. The strong scent attracts the night moths, they cross-pollinate the flowers, which eventually wither. The sea lily blooms in August-September (two months before emergence of its new leaves) thus closing the flowering cycle and opening a new season of flowers.